CONTENTS

UNIT		PAGE
	How the book is set out	4
	How to use this book	5
1	How many fit inside?	6
2	Which shape is similar?	8
3	Find the shaded fraction	10
4	Which one is different?	12
5	Find the shaded fraction of equal value	14
6	Where is it hidden?	16
7	What comes next?	18
8	Give the next number (addition and subtraction series)	20
9	Which shape is the same but facing the opposite direction?	22
10	How does it look, folded in?	26
11	Give the next number (multiplication and division series)	28
12	How does it look, opened out?	30
13	What shape now, after adding?	32
14	Supply the missing numbers	34
15	What shape now, after subtracting?	36
16	Which completes the matching pair? (analogies)	38
17	Which two shapes are exactly the same?	40
18	Fill in the addition table	42
	How well did you do?	44
	Detachable Answers	45

HOW THE BOOK IS SET OUT

• There are eighteen different topics.

• Each one is dealt with in a separate unit.

• Each unit has two sections:-
1. The INTRODUCTION with a worked Example and Step by Step instructions.
2. The EXERCISE with some Hints for extra help.

• A detachable answers sheet is provided at the back.

HOW TO USE THIS BOOK

1.   Do the units in order, as they are graded.

2.   Read the INTRODUCTION 2 or 3 times to understand the example.

3.   Do the EXERCISE on your own.

4.   Use the STEP by STEP section and the Hints provided.

5.   If you change an answer, make sure the change is clear.

6.   Each exercise should take between 5 and 10 minutes.

7.   Do not rush!

8.   When you have finished each unit, mark it with an adult.

9.   Enter your score out of 10 at the end of each exercise.

10.   Fill in your score on the bar chart on page 44.

UNIT 1

HOW MANY FIT INSIDE?

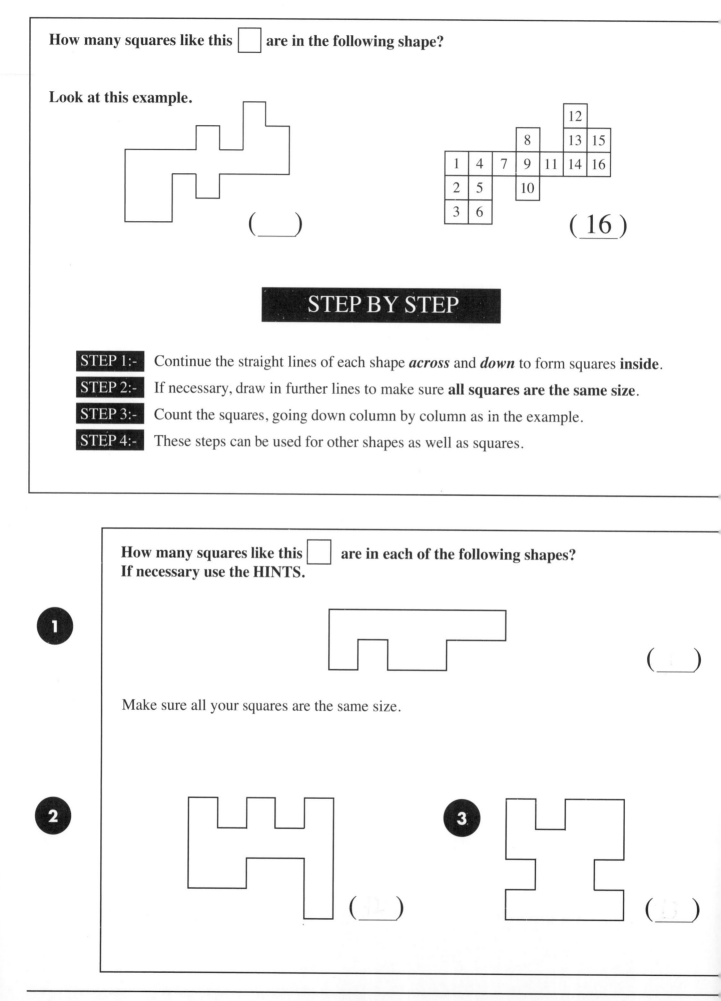

How many squares like this ☐ are in the following shape?

Look at this example.

(_)

(16)

STEP BY STEP

STEP 1:- Continue the straight lines of each shape *across* and *down* to form squares **inside**.

STEP 2:- If necessary, draw in further lines to make sure **all squares are the same size**.

STEP 3:- Count the squares, going down column by column as in the example.

STEP 4:- These steps can be used for other shapes as well as squares.

How many squares like this ☐ are in each of the following shapes?
If necessary use the **HINTS**.

1

(_)

Make sure all your squares are the same size.

2

(_)

3

(_)

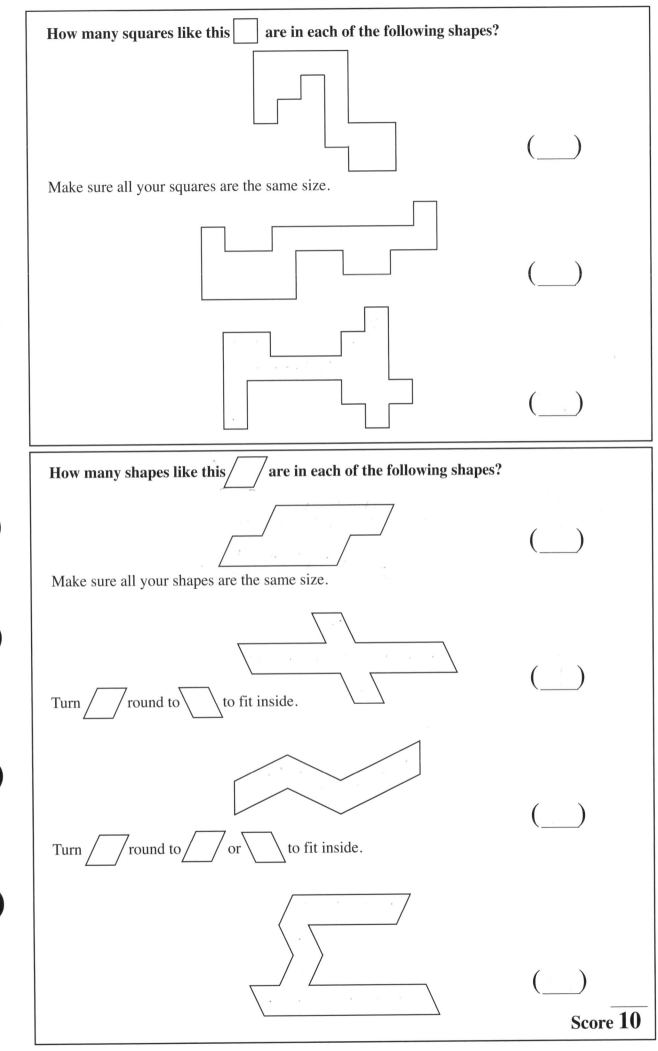

4

How many squares like this ☐ **are in each of the following shapes?**

(   )

Make sure all your squares are the same size.

5

(   )

6

(   )

How many shapes like this ⃕ **are in each of the following shapes?**

7

Make sure all your shapes are the same size.

(   )

8

Turn ⃕ round to ⃔ to fit inside.

(   )

9

Turn ⃕ round to ⃕ or ⃔ to fit inside.

(   )

10

(   )

Score 10

UNIT 2   WHICH SHAPE IS SIMILAR?

Which shape is similar to the group of three on the left? Circle one letter. Look at this example.

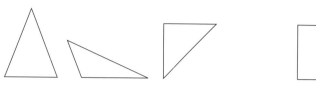
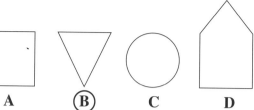

The answer is **B** because:-
Like the three shapes on the left, B is a triangle.

Not A, a square.
Not C, a circle.
Not D, a pentagon.

STEP BY STEP

THINGS TO LOOK FOR:-

• THE TYPES, COLOURS AND/OR NUMBER OF SHAPES

• THE POSITION OF THE SHAPES AND/OR THE SYMBOLS

STEP 1:- Find what makes each group of three similar.

STEP 2:- Ignore any answers that are obviously wrong.

STEP 3:- Make sure your chosen answer matches the group of three in **every way**.

Which shape is similar to the group of three on the left? Circle one letter each time. If necessary use the HINTS.

1    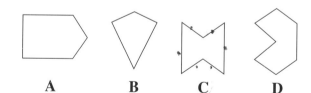

Count the number of sides.

2   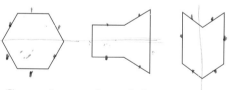 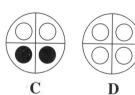

Look at the colours of the small circles.

3   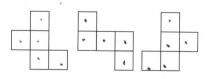 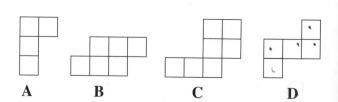

Count the number of squares.

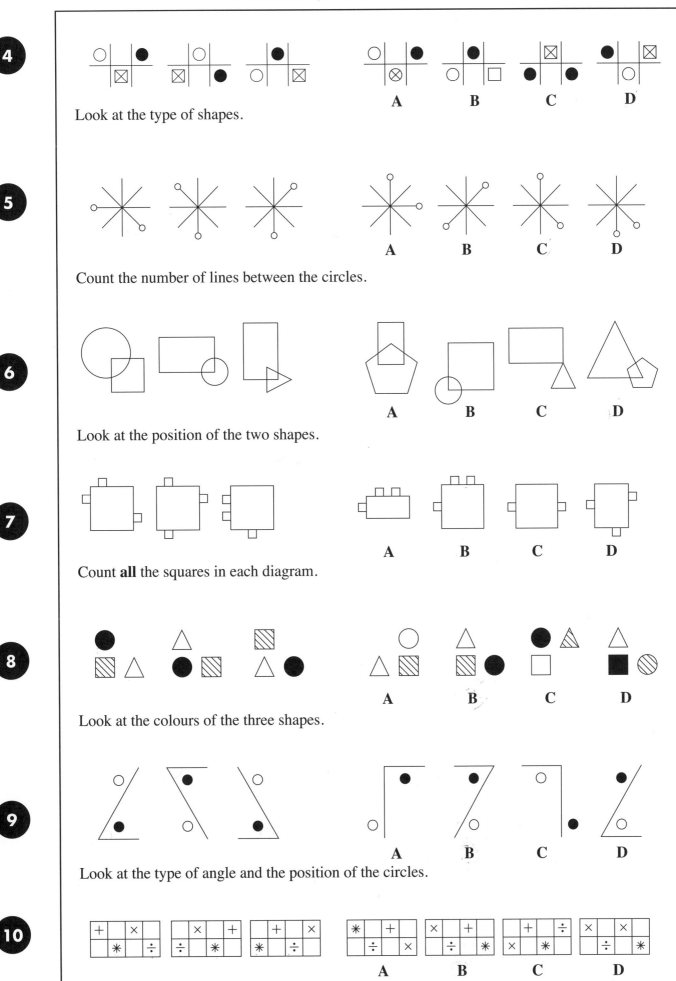

4

Look at the type of shapes.

A   B   C   D

5

Count the number of lines between the circles.

A   B   C   D

6

Look at the position of the two shapes.

A   B   C   D

7

Count **all** the squares in each diagram.

A   B   C   D

8

Look at the colours of the three shapes.

A   B   C   D

9

Look at the type of angle and the position of the circles.

A   B   C   D

10

Look at the position and the types of symbols.

A   B   C   D

Score **10**

UNIT 3   FIND THE SHADED FRACTION

Find the SHADED fraction. Circle one answer. Look at this example.

$$\frac{3}{7} \quad \frac{5}{8} \quad \frac{8}{3} \quad \boxed{\frac{3}{8}}$$

The answer is $\frac{3}{8}$ because:-

three out of eight equal triangles are shaded.

Not $\frac{3}{7}$, there are **8** equal parts, after the bottom rectangle is divided into two triangles, as shown above.

Not $\frac{5}{8}$, this is the **unshaded** fraction.

Not $\frac{8}{3}$, the shaded part is always the **top** number of the fraction.

STEP BY STEP

THINGS TO LOOK FOR:-

• THE WHOLE SHAPE MAY BE DIVIDED UP INTO A NUMBER OF PARTS THAT ARE **NOT** ALWAYS EQUAL

• DO **NOT** SHADE ANY OF THE SHAPES

STEP 1:- Check that all the parts are of equal shape and size.

STEP 2:- To make all the parts equal, draw in lines across, down and/or diagonally **inside** the shape.

STEP 3:- To find the top number of the fraction, count the equal **shaded** parts.

STEP 4:- To find the bottom number of the fraction count **all** the equal parts, shaded **and** unshaded.

Find the shaded fraction. Circle one answer each time.
If necessary use the HINTS.

1

$$\frac{1}{5} \quad \frac{5}{7} \quad \frac{5}{6} \quad \frac{1}{6}$$

2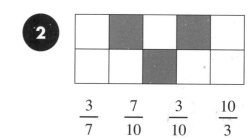

$$\frac{3}{7} \quad \frac{7}{10} \quad \frac{3}{10} \quad \frac{10}{3}$$

Count the shaded squares and then count all the squares.

3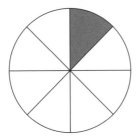

$$\frac{1}{8} \quad \frac{1}{6} \quad \frac{1}{7} \quad \frac{1}{5}$$

Count the parts of the circle.

4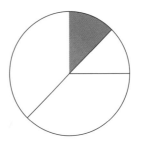

$$\frac{1}{4} \quad \frac{1}{6} \quad \frac{1}{8} \quad \frac{1}{5}$$

Make all parts of the circle equal.

5

$$\frac{2}{5} \quad \frac{1}{3} \quad \frac{1}{6} \quad \frac{1}{4}$$

6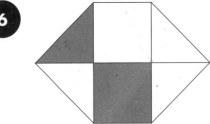

$$\frac{2}{6} \quad \frac{3}{8} \quad \frac{1}{2} \quad \frac{3}{7}$$

Make all parts into triangles of equal size.

7

$$\frac{4}{9} \quad \frac{1}{2} \quad \frac{5}{11} \quad \frac{3}{7}$$

Make all parts into triangles of equal size.

8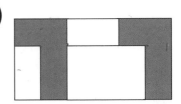

$$\frac{3}{8} \quad \frac{4}{9} \quad \frac{4}{7} \quad \frac{2}{5}$$

Make all parts into rectangles of equal size.

9

$$\frac{7}{12} \quad \frac{6}{11} \quad \frac{7}{9} \quad \frac{5}{7}$$

Make all parts into squares of equal size.

10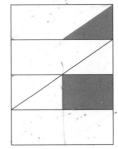

$$\frac{2}{7} \quad \frac{5}{12} \quad \frac{3}{5} \quad \frac{3}{16}$$

Make all parts into triangles of equal size.

Score 10

UNIT 4

WHICH ONE IS DIFFERENT?

Which one is different from the other four? Circle one letter.
Look at this example.

A   B   C   D   E

The answer is E because:-
It is the only shape with **three** sides.

STEP BY STEP

THINGS TO LOOK FOR:-
- THE TYPES OF SHAPES AND/OR LINES
- THE NUMBER OF SIDES AND/OR SYMBOLS
- THE SIZE OR POSITION OF THE SHAPES

STEP 1:- Look for similarities in each diagram.
STEP 2:- Find a pattern in the similarities.
STEP 3:- Which one is different and why?

Which one is different from the other four? Circle one letter each time.
If necessary use the HINTS.

1

           A   B   C   D   E

Compare the two shapes in each diagram.

2

           A   B   C   D   E

Look at the different signs.

3   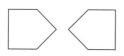   

           A   B   C   D   E

Look how each pair is matching.

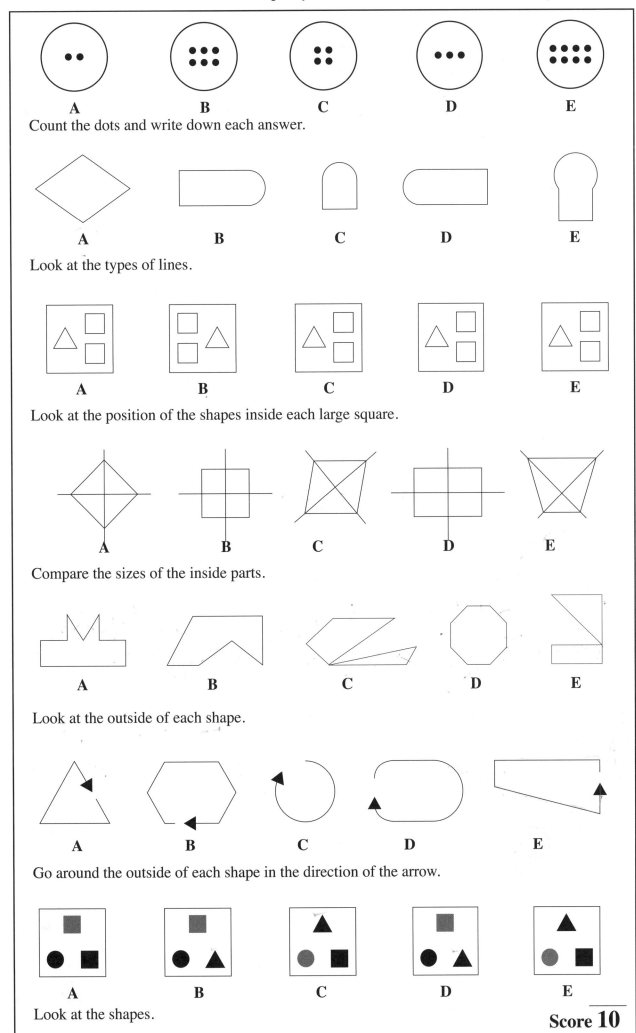

4 Count the dots and write down each answer.

5 Look at the types of lines.

6 Look at the position of the shapes inside each large square.

7 Compare the sizes of the inside parts.

8 Look at the outside of each shape.

9 Go around the outside of each shape in the direction of the arrow.

10 Look at the shapes.

Score 10

UNIT 5   FIND THE SHADED FRACTION OF EQUAL VALUE

Find the SHADED fraction of equal value. Circle one answer. Look at this example.

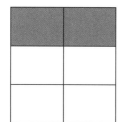

$$\frac{2}{6} = \frac{1}{3}$$

$$\frac{2}{5} \qquad \frac{2}{3} \qquad \frac{1}{2} \qquad \boxed{\frac{1}{3}}$$

The answer is $\frac{1}{3}$ because:-

The shaded fraction is $\frac{2}{6}$ and $\frac{2}{6}$ is equal in value to $\frac{1}{3}$.

Not $\frac{2}{5}$, there are **6** equal parts.

Not $\frac{2}{3}$, as $\frac{4}{6}$ is the **unshaded** fraction.

Not $\frac{1}{2}$, as $\frac{3}{6}$ is **not** the **shaded** fraction.

STEP BY STEP

THINGS TO LOOK FOR:-

- MAKE ALL PARTS OF EQUAL SHAPE AND SIZE TO FIND THE SHADED FRACTION
- DIVIDE BOTH TOP AND BOTTOM NUMBERS OF THE FRACTION BY THE SAME NUMBER
- IF YOU DON'T FIND THE ANSWER, CHECK YOUR DIVISION IN STEP 3.

STEP 1:- **Write down** the shaded fraction.

STEP 2:- Find **one** number that divides **exactly** into **both** the top and bottom numbers of the fraction.

STEP 3:- Divide them both by this number, and write down the new top and bottom numbers.

STEP 4:- Repeat Steps 2 and 3 if necessary to find the correct answer.

Find the SHADED fraction of equal value. Circle one answer each time. If necessary use the HINTS.

 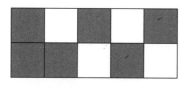

$$\frac{2}{3} \qquad \frac{3}{5} \qquad \frac{3}{10} \qquad \frac{5}{9}$$

$$\frac{1}{4} \qquad \frac{1}{7} \qquad \frac{2}{5} \qquad \frac{1}{2}$$

Divide the top and bottom numbers of the shaded fraction by 2.

3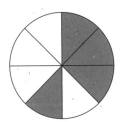

$$\frac{1}{2} \qquad \frac{2}{5} \qquad \frac{1}{4} \qquad \frac{1}{3}$$

Make sure all parts of the circle are of equal size.

4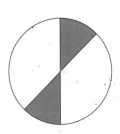

$$\frac{1}{2} \qquad \frac{2}{5} \qquad \frac{1}{4} \qquad \frac{1}{3}$$

5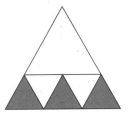

$$\frac{1}{3} \qquad \frac{1}{2} \qquad \frac{3}{7} \qquad \frac{3}{8}$$

6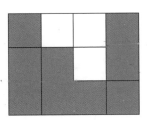

$$\frac{2}{3} \qquad \frac{3}{4} \qquad \frac{5}{7} \qquad \frac{4}{5}$$

Make all parts of equal shape and size and then divide by 3.

7

$$\frac{3}{4} \qquad \frac{4}{5} \qquad \frac{2}{3} \qquad \frac{5}{7}$$

8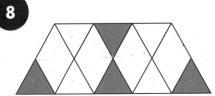

$$\frac{1}{4} \qquad \frac{1}{5} \qquad \frac{1}{3} \qquad \frac{4}{11}$$

Make all parts into triangles of equal size. Use Step 4, if needed.

9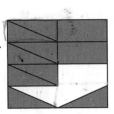

$$\frac{2}{3} \qquad \frac{9}{11} \qquad \frac{3}{4} \qquad \frac{11}{14}$$

10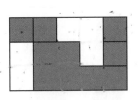

$$\frac{5}{8} \qquad \frac{3}{4} \qquad \frac{1}{2} \qquad \frac{2}{3}$$

Make all parts of equal shape and size.

Score $\underline{10}$

UNIT 6

WHERE IS IT HIDDEN?

Which larger shape is the small shape on the left hidden in? Circle one letter. Look at this example.

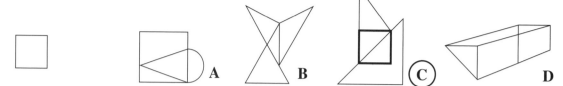

The square is hidden in C.

Not A,   the square is too big.
Not B or D,   they do not contain
squares.

STEP BY STEP

THINGS TO LOOK FOR:-

• THE HIDDEN SHAPE MAY HAVE LINES INSIDE IT

• IT MAY HAVE BEEN TURNED ROUND BUT NOT OVER

• IT MUST BE EXACTLY THE SAME SIZE

STEP 1:- Describe the shape to be hidden.

STEP 2:- Note the number of sides, length of lines and types of angles.

STEP 3:- Outline the hidden shape on your chosen answer.

STEP 4:- If necessary turn the shape round to help you find it.

Which larger shape is the small shape on the left hidden in? Circle one letter each time.
If necessary use the HINTS.

1 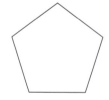 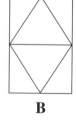   A   B   C   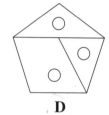

The pentagon does not turn.

2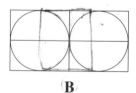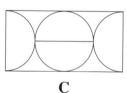

Two semi-circles are touching.

3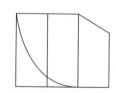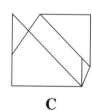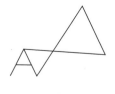

Small triangle at the top with the letter A below.

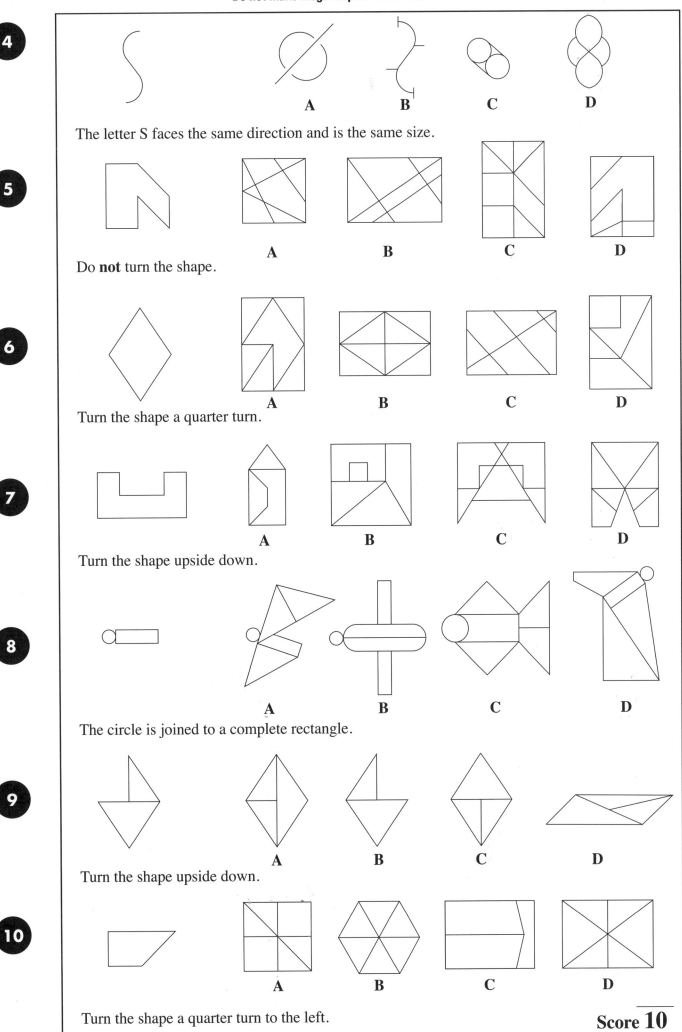

4

The letter S faces the same direction and is the same size.

5

Do **not** turn the shape.

6

Turn the shape a quarter turn.

7

Turn the shape upside down.

8

The circle is joined to a complete rectangle.

9

Turn the shape upside down.

10

Turn the shape a quarter turn to the left.

Score 10

UNIT 7   WHAT COMES NEXT?

What comes next in this series? Circle one letter.
Look at this example.

                                                           (A)   B   C   D

The answer is **A** because:-
The colour series is white, white, white, black, black, black.
The shape series is circle, square, triangle, circle, square, triangle.

STEP BY STEP

THINGS TO LOOK FOR:-
• CHANGES IN COLOUR, SHAPE OR SIZE
• CHANGES IN POSITION OR NUMBER OF SYMBOLS
• A MIXTURE OF THESE OR OTHER CHANGES

STEP 1:- Look at general changes and similarities, between each diagram.

STEP 2:- Look for a pattern in the changes.

STEP 3:- Do the different changes **one at a time.**

STEP 4:- Which one comes next and why?

What comes next in each series? Circle one letter each time.
If necessary use the HINTS.

1

                                                       A   B   C   D

Which corner of the square has not been shaded?

2   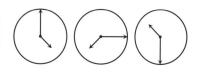   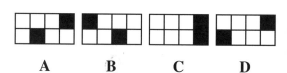

                                                       A   B   C   D

One shaded square does not move.

3      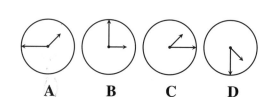

                                                       A   B   C   D

The hands move clockwise through a quarter turn.

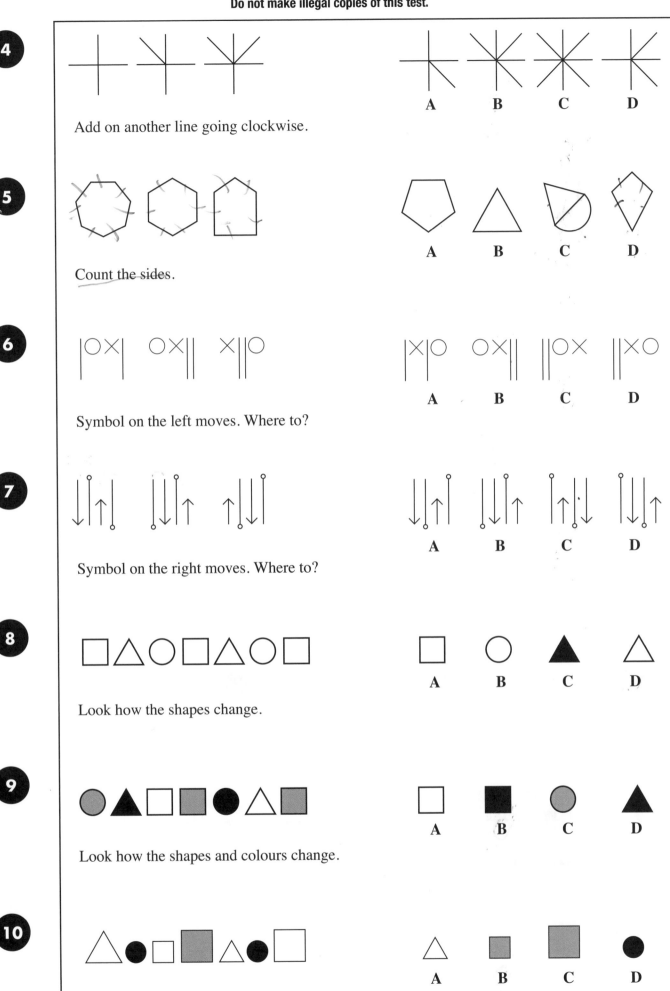

4 Add on another line going clockwise.

A   B   C   D

5 Count the sides.

A   B   C   D

6 Symbol on the left moves. Where to?

A   B   C   D

7 Symbol on the right moves. Where to?

A   B   C   D

8 Look how the shapes change.

A   B   C   D

9 Look how the shapes and colours change.

A   B   C   D

10 Look how the shapes, colours and size change.

A   B   C   D

Score 10

UNIT 8
GIVE THE NEXT NUMBER
(ADDITION AND SUBTRACTION SERIES)

Give the next number in each series.

Look at these examples.

$$35, 40, 45, 50, 55, \ (\underline{60})$$

The answer is 60 because:-

The series is going up in 5's and 55+5=60.

$$50, 40, 32, 26, 22, \ (\underline{20})$$

The answer is 20 because:-

In this series the number taken away is going down in twos,
(-10, -8, -6, -4, now -2) and 22-2=20.

STEP BY STEP

THINGS TO LOOK FOR:-
• SERIES GOING UP ARE **ADDITION** PATTERNS
• SERIES GOING DOWN ARE **SUBTRACTION** PATTERNS
• SERIES GOING UP AND DOWN ARE MIXED ADDITION AND SUBTRACTION PATTERNS
• IF THERE SEEMS TO BE NO PATTERN, CHECK YOUR SUBTRACTION IN STEP 1
• DO NOT WRITE DOWN THE PATTERN AS THE ANSWER

STEP 1:- Find the difference between each pair of numbers.

STEP 2:- Write the answers from STEP 1 in between each pair of numbers.

STEP 3:- Find the addition and/or subtraction pattern.

STEP 4:- Find the next number by using this pattern.

Give the next number in each series. If necessary use the HINTS.

1 4, 13, 22, 31, 40, (___)

By how many do the numbers increase each time?

2 5, 6, 8, 11, 15, (___)

The number added is increasing by one each time.

3 3, 7, 13, 21, 31, (___)

The number added is increasing by two each time.

4 1, 2, 5, 10, 17, (___)

5 6, 7, 11, 12, 16, (___)

Two different numbers are added and each one is repeated in turn.

6 12, 14, 17, 19, 22, (___)

7 61, 53, 45, 37, 29, (___)

By how many do the numbers go down each time?

8 90, 76, 63, 51, 40, (___)

The number taken away is going down by one each time.

9 90, 75, 62, 51, 42, (___)

The number taken away is going down by two each time.

10 31, 29, 32, 30, 33, (___)

Mixed addition and subtraction pattern and each one is repeated in turn.

Score 10

UNIT 9

WHICH SHAPE IS THE SAME,
BUT FACING THE OPPOSITE DIRECTION?

Working through these two pages will help you to complete the questions on pages 24 and 25.

Look at the completed Learning Together picture above.
Now join up the dotted lines and shade in the one below, so that it looks exactly the same.

Look across both ways,——→ and ←——, to see how you have made the SAME SHAPE as before,
but FACING THE OPPOSITE DIRECTION.

The following page will help to explain this further.

This unit is like Mirror Image, which you may have done in Mathematics at school. Letters of the alphabet make good examples.

• YOU CAN SEE HOW DIAGONAL LINES FACE THE OPPOSITE DIRECTION:-

LETTER   FACING THE OPPOSITE DIRECTION

K   K
Z   Z
N   N

• CURVED LINES ALSO FACE THE OPPOSITE DIRECTION:-

C   C
J   J
S   S

• SOME LETTERS STAY THE SAME:-

A   A
O   O
X   X

This is because when you split them down the middle, they match perfectly. (They are vertically symmetrical):-e.g.

A

• HORIZONTAL LINES SWOP SIDES:-

L   L
F   F
E   E

• GROUPS OF LETTERS (OR SHAPES) ALSO SWOP SIDES:-

AMIT   AMIT
JEFF   JEFF
CHLOE   CHLOE

• WRITE YOUR NAME BELOW IN **CAPITALS**:-   NOW WRITE IT FACING THE OPPOSITE DIRECTION

_____   _____

TO CHECK, WRITE YOUR NAME AGAIN ON A THIN TRANSPARENT PIECE OF PAPER, AND TURN IT OVER!

Now begin the unit starting on page 24.

WHICH SHAPE IS THE SAME, BUT FACING THE OPPOSITE DIRECTION?

Which shape is the same as the one on the left, but facing the opposite direction? Circle one letter. Look at this example.

         A   **B**   **C**   **D**   **(E)**

The answer is E because:-
It is exactly the same shape but the opposite way round.
The shaded angle now points in the opposite direction.

Not A ⎤
Not B ⎥ in all these shapes the
Not C ⎥ shaded angle points
Not D ⎦ up or down.

STEP BY STEP

STEP 1:- Find all the lines and/or shapes that change.

STEP 2:- Work out how they look, facing the opposite direction.

STEP 3:- Ignore any answers which are obviously wrong.

STEP 4:- Which *one* answer now fits?

Which shape is the same as the one on the left, but facing the opposite direction. Circle one letter each time. If necessary use the HINTS.

1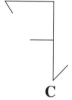

         A   **B**   **C**   **D**

The horizontal and diagonal lines point in the opposite direction.

2

         A   **B**   **C**   **D**   **E**

Look at the diagonal lines first.

3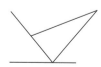

         A   **B**   **C**   **D**

As well as the triangle, the long and short lines each side of the bottom point change sides.

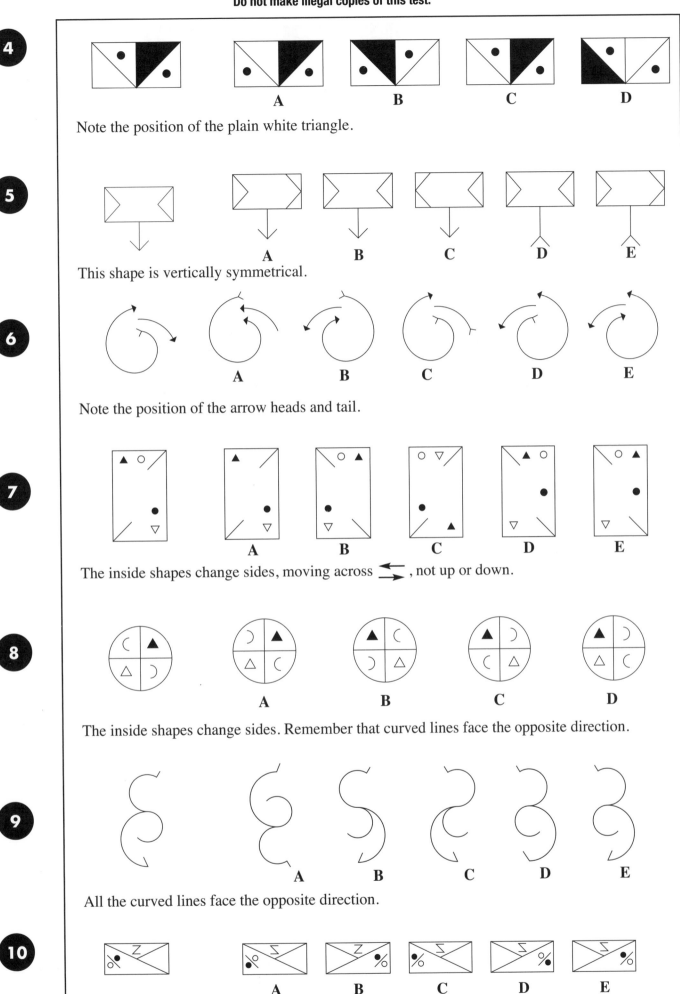

4

Note the position of the plain white triangle.

5

This shape is vertically symmetrical.

6

Note the position of the arrow heads and tail.

7

The inside shapes change sides, moving across, not up or down.

8

The inside shapes change sides. Remember that curved lines face the opposite direction.

9

All the curved lines face the opposite direction.

10

All the diagonals face the opposite direction.

Score **10**

UNIT 10 HOW DOES IT LOOK FOLDED IN?

How does the shape on the left look, folded in? Circle one letter. Look at this example.

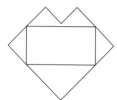

A   (B)   C   D

The answer is **B** because:-

When the 4 flaps are opened out again, they form the given shape, with the flap that is not a complete triangle on the top.

Not A, the triangle on the bottom is not complete.
Not C, and
Not D, all the triangles are complete.

STEP BY STEP

THINGS TO LOOK FOR:-

• IN A SOLID, NOTE THE NUMBER OF FACES AND THE SHAPE OF THE BASE

• IN A SHAPE WITH FLAPS, THEY FOLD IN →▼◀ TO GIVE THE SAME SHAPE IN THE OPPOSITE DIRECTION

• THE SHAPES DO NOT TURN

STEP 1:- How do the faces or flaps of the shape fold in?

STEP 2:- Count the number of faces or flaps.

STEP 3:- Note also the shape and/or colour of each one.

STEP 4:- Which *one* answer now fits?

How does the shape on the left look, folded in? Circle one letter each time. If necessary use the HINTS.

1 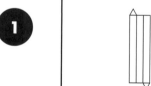 Gives

A   B   C   D

Look at the number of faces and their shape.

2 Gives

A   B   C   D

Make sure the base has the correct shape and position.

3 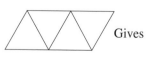  Gives

A   B   C   D

Make sure the base has the correct shape. Look at the number of faces.

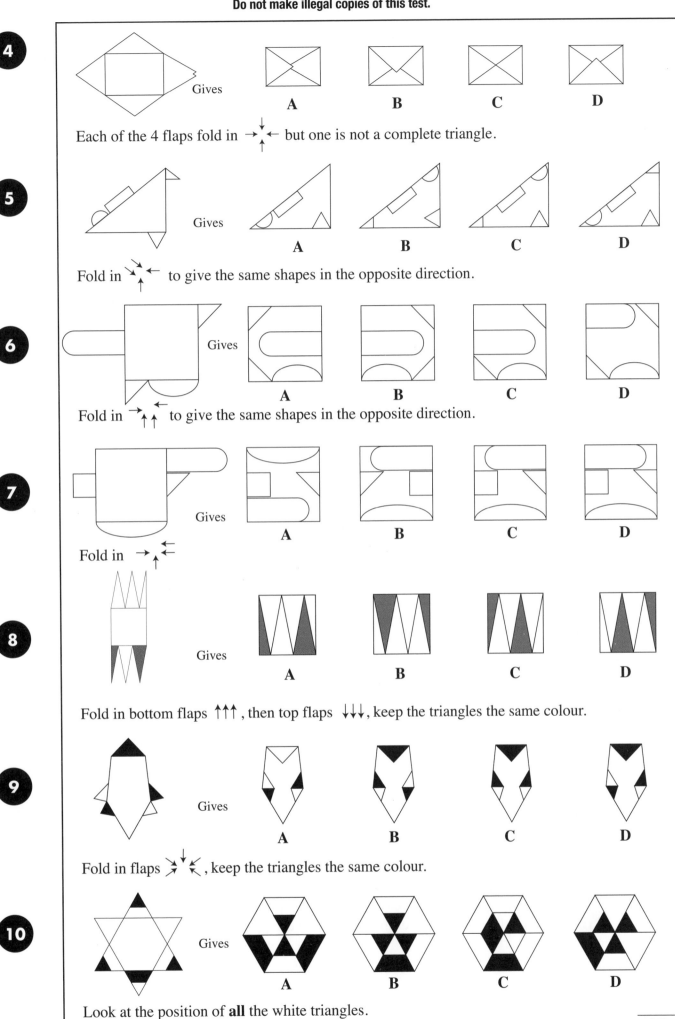

4

Gives   **A**   **B**   **C**   **D**

Each of the 4 flaps fold in →↓←↑ but one is not a complete triangle.

5

Gives   **A**   **B**   **C**   **D**

Fold in ↘↓←↑ to give the same shapes in the opposite direction.

6

Gives   **A**   **B**   **C**   **D**

Fold in →↑↑← to give the same shapes in the opposite direction.

7

Gives   **A**   **B**   **C**   **D**

Fold in →↑←←

8

Gives   **A**   **B**   **C**   **D**

Fold in bottom flaps ↑↑↑, then top flaps ↓↓↓, keep the triangles the same colour.

9

Gives   **A**   **B**   **C**   **D**

Fold in flaps ↗↓↙, keep the triangles the same colour.

10

Gives   **A**   **B**   **C**   **D**

Look at the position of **all** the white triangles.

Score 10

UNIT 11

GIVE THE NEXT NUMBER
(MULTIPLICATION AND DIVISION SERIES)

Give the next number in each series.

Look at these examples.

$$2, 4, 8, 16, 32, \ (\underline{64})$$

The answer is 64 because:-

In this series each number is being multiplied by 2, and 32 x 2 = 64.

$$64, 32, 16, 8, 4, \ (\underline{2})$$

The answer is 2 because:-

In this series each number is being divided by 2, and 4 ÷ 2 = 2.

STEP BY STEP

THINGS TO LOOK FOR:-

- SERIES GOING UP ARE **MULTIPLICATION** PATTERNS
- SERIES GOING DOWN ARE **DIVISION** PATTERNS
- IF THERE SEEMS TO BE NO PATTERN, CHECK YOUR DIVISION SUM IN STEPS 1 OR 2
- DO NOT WRITE DOWN THE PATTERN AS THE ANSWER

STEP 1:- For series going up, divide the **first** 2 pairs of numbers into each other.

STEP 2:- For series going down, divide the **last** 2 pairs of numbers into each other.

STEP 3:- The answers from Steps 1 and 2 give the multiplication or division pattern.

STEP 4:- Find the next number in the series by using this pattern.

Give the next number in each series. If necessary use the HINTS.

1 5, 10, 20, 40, 80,   (___)

$10 \div 5$ gives the pattern.

2 9, 18, 36, 72, 144,   (___)

3 1, 3, 9, 27, 81,   (___)

4 (6, 12) (8, 16) (10, 20) (12, 24)   (14, ___)

How do the numbers inside the brackets increase?

5 (1, 7) (3, 21) (5, 35) (7, 49)   (9, ___)

6 96, 48, 24, 12, 6,   (___)

$12 \div 6$ gives the pattern.

7 729, 243, 81, 27, 9,   (___)

Use the answer to $27 \div 9$ to find $81 \div 27$.

8 972, 324, 108, 36, 12,   (___)

Use the answer to $36 \div 12$ to find $108 \div 36$.

9 (48, 24) (40, 20) (32, 16) (24, 12) (16, ___)

How do the numbers inside the brackets decrease?

10 (48, 12) (40, 10) (32, 8) (24, 6)   (16, ___)

Score 10

UNIT 12   HOW DOES IT LOOK OPENED OUT?

How does the shape on the left look, opened out? Circle one letter.
Look at this example.

A   **B**   **C**   **D**

The answer is **C** because:-
When the 6 squares are folded in, they make the cube.

Not A, it has only 5 squares.
Not B or D, they do not have one square on each side
of a line of 4 squares.

STEP BY STEP

THINGS TO LOOK FOR:-

• IN A SOLID, THE "TOP" AND "BOTTOM" FACES MUST BE ON OPPOSITE SIDES

• IN A SHAPE WITH FLAPS, THEY OPEN OUT → ↓↑ ← TO GIVE THE SAME SHAPE IN THE OPPOSITE DIRECTION

• THE SHAPES DO NOT TURN

STEP 1:- How do the faces or flaps of the shapes open out?

STEP 2:- Count the number of faces or flaps.

STEP 3:- Note also the shape and/or colour of each one.

STEP 4:- Which *one* answer now fits?

How does the shape on the left look, opened out? Circle one letter each time.
If necessary use the HINTS.

1   Gives   **A**   **B**   **C**   **D**

A cube and a cuboid both have 6 faces, the top and the bottom are on opposite sides.

2   Gives   **A**   **B**   **C**   **D**

3   Gives   **A**   **B**   **C**   **D**

The base is square, each pair of triangles must be on opposite sides to each other.

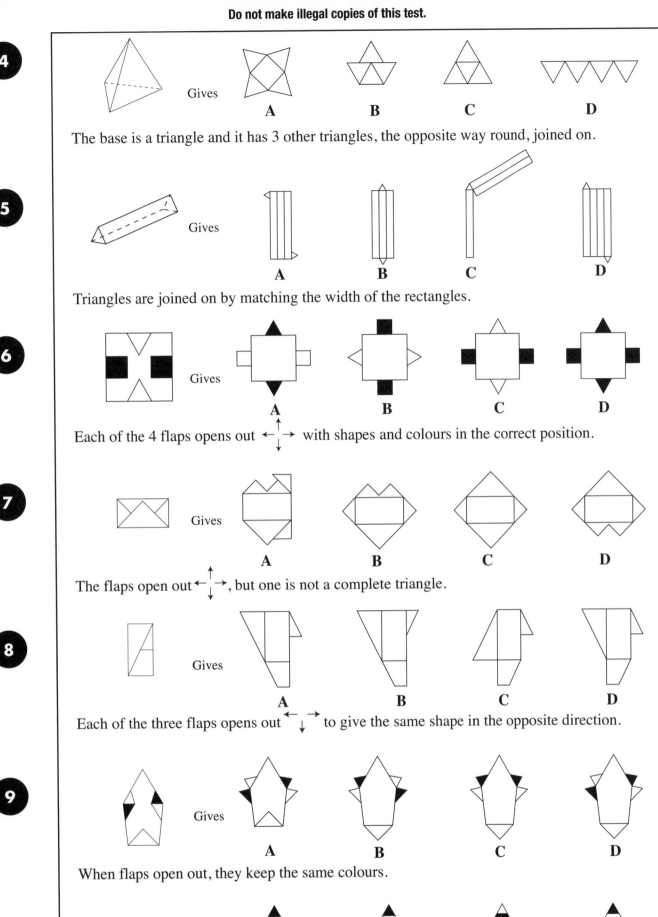

4

Gives

A **B** **C** **D**

The base is a triangle and it has 3 other triangles, the opposite way round, joined on.

5

Gives

A **B** **C** **D**

Triangles are joined on by matching the width of the rectangles.

6

Gives

A **B** **C** **D**

Each of the 4 flaps opens out ←↑↓→ with shapes and colours in the correct position.

7

Gives

A **B** **C** **D**

The flaps open out ←↑↓→, but one is not a complete triangle.

8

Gives

A **B** **C** **D**

Each of the three flaps opens out ←↓→ to give the same shape in the opposite direction.

9

Gives

A **B** **C** **D**

When flaps open out, they keep the same colours.

10

Gives

A **B** **C** **D**

Look at the position of **all** the white triangles.

Score 10

UNIT 13   WHAT SHAPE NOW AFTER ADDING?

In these questions the two shapes are added together.
The shapes do not turn. Circle one letter. Look at this example.

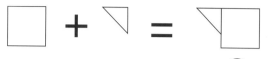

       (A)   **B**   **C**   **D**

The answer is A because:-
The small triangle has been added to the top left hand
corner of the square.

Not B, the triangle has been subtracted,
Not C, the triangle has been turned,
Not D, one line of the triangle is missing.

STEP BY STEP

THINGS TO LOOK FOR:-

• ONE SHAPE MAY LIE PARTLY ON TOP OF THE OTHER
• LINES MAY MERGE TO BECOME ONE LINE
• BLACK AND WHITE SHAPES MERGE TO BECOME BLACK

STEP 1:- Work out where and how the second shape is added.

STEP 2:- Make sure the two shapes do not change when they are put together.

STEP 3:- Draw the outline of **one** of the shapes on your chosen answer.

STEP 4:- Check that what is left is the same as the **other** shape.

In these questions the two shapes are added together. The shapes do *not* turn.
Circle one letter each time. If necessary use the HINTS.

 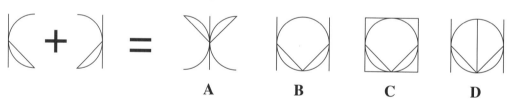

                 A   **B**   **C**   **D**

Look at the number and type of straight lines in the 2 shapes.

 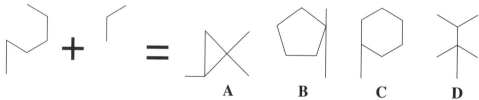

                 A   **B**   **C**   **D**

Make the shape on the left complete.

 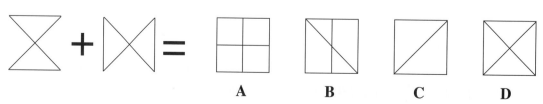

                 A   **B**   **C**   **D**

The diagonals lie on top of each other.

4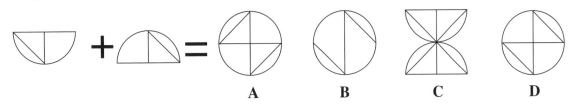

Keep the same number of diagonal lines and merge the horizontal ones.

5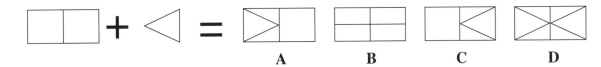

The tip of the triangle is on the left.

6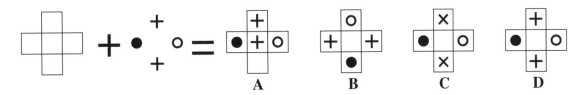

Keep the symbols in the same positions.

7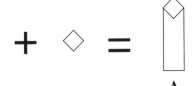

Two lines merge when the shapes join.

8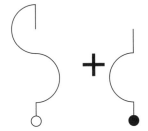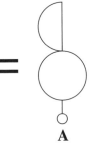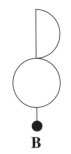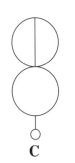

Find the correct shape at the top and correct colour at the bottom.

9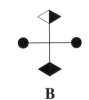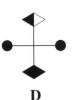

After merging, decide what remains white.

10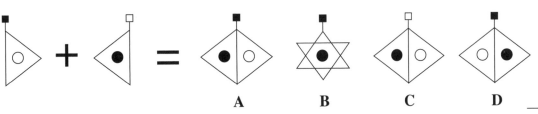

The vertical lines and the squares merge.

Score 10

UNIT 14   SUPPLY THE MISSING NUMBERS

Supply the missing numbers. Look at this example.

```
  8 □ 3            8 5 3
  2 3 4            2 3 4
+ 1 9 4          + 1 9 4
─────────        ─────────
1 2 8 1          1 2 8 1
                   1   1
```

STEP BY STEP

THINGS TO LOOK FOR:-

• EACH BOX NEEDS ONLY ONE NUMBER

• THE MISSING NUMBER CAN BE ZERO   0

STEP 1:- Add the numbers in each column starting with the units column.

STEP 2:- For each column write any carrying figure below the line of the next column.

STEP 3:- Add the carrying figures to the other numbers in the columns before finding the missing numbers.

STEP 4:- What number must be in the box and added on to give the number on the answer line?

Supply the missing numbers. If necessary use the HINTS.

 1

```
  7 5 2
  5 4 □
+ 3 8 1
─────────
1 6 7 6
```

2

```
  2 2 8
  3 6 5
+ 4 7 □
─────────
1 0 6 5
```

Unit column: 2+□+1=6

Unit column: 8+5+□=15

3

```
    6 3 7
    9 8 0
+ 1 □ 9
─────────
1 7 6 6
```

4

```
    1 5 4
  □ 9 8
+ 7 2 1
─────────
1 7 7 3
```

Write the carrying figures below the next columns and add them on, **before** finding the missing numbers.

5

```
  8 □ 6
  3 1 4
+ 5 1 □
─────────
1 6 9 1
```

6

```
  8 □ 9
  5 7 4
+ □ 1 3
─────────
1 5 9 6
```

No carrying figure to the hundreds column.

Missing number can be zero.

7

```
    1 7 8
    5 1 6
+ 8 5 2
─────────
1 5 □ 6
```

8

```
    2 6 7
    9 7 2
+ 5 1 4
─────────
1 □ 5 3
```

Add each column as in an ordinary sum.

9

```
    2 4 8
  □ 6 3
+ 1 4 2
─────────
□ 1 5 3
```

10

```
    4 □ 5
  □ 8 2
+ 1 7 7
─────────
□ 2 8 4
```

Score 10

UNIT 15

WHAT SHAPE NOW AFTER SUBTRACTING?

In these questions one shape is subtracted from the other.
The shapes do not turn. Circle one letter. Look at this example.

The answer is B because:-
The corner cut off matches exactly the triangle to be subtracted:

NOT A   as it has been added.
NOT C ⌐ as different triangles have
NOT D ⌐ been subtracted.

STEP BY STEP

THINGS TO LOOK FOR:-

• THE SHAPE TO BE SUBTRACTED MUST NOT TURN

• SUBTRACTING THE SECOND SHAPE IS LIKE "CUTTING IT OUT" OF THE FIRST SHAPE

STEP 1:- Find where and how the second shape is "cut out" of the first shape.

STEP 2:- Draw the outline of the shape to be subtracted inside the first shape, as in the example.

STEP 3:- Which answer matches the shape that is left after subtracting?

In these questions one shape is subtracted from the other. The shapes do not turn.
Circle one letter each time. If necessary use the HINTS.

1

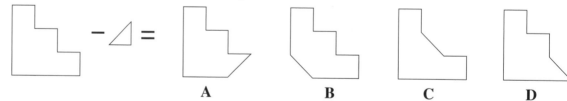

Cut off the correct corner to match the triangle that is subtracted.

2

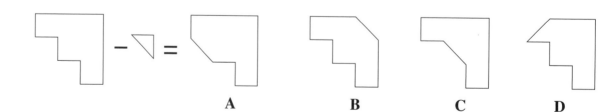

The same triangle as the second shape must be subtracted, not added.

3

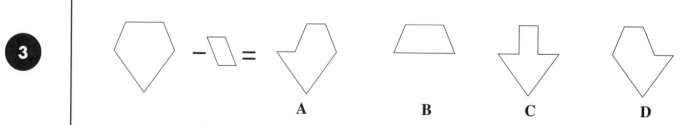

The diagonal sides of the shape to be subtracted must go in the same direction.

4

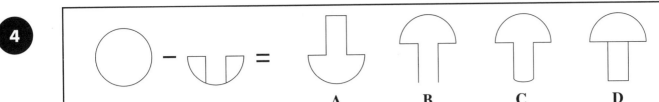

Work out what remains when the second shape is "cut out" of the first.

5

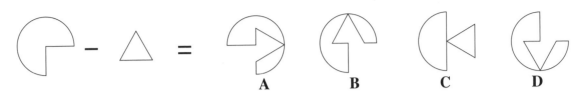

"Cut out" the same shaped triangle. Do not turn the triangle.

6

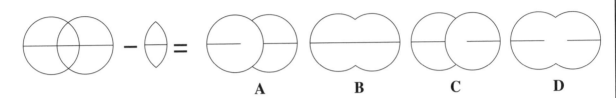

Take away the round lines inside and the short straight line in between them.

7

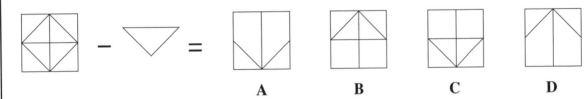

Take away *all three* sides of the correct triangle.

8

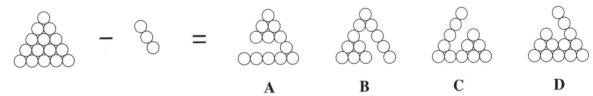

Make sure the pattern of *three* circles goes in the same direction.

9

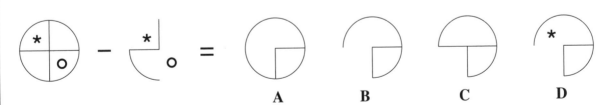

Take away the correct outside part of the circle and the correct two lines inside.

10

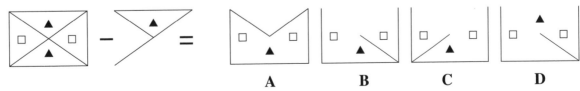

Take away the large and small triangles at the top and the correct diagonal at the bottom.

Score 10

UNIT 16 WHICH SHAPE COMPLETES THE MATCHING PAIR? (ANALOGIES)

Which shape completes the matching pair? Match the second pair of shapes in the same way as the first. Circle one letter. Look at this example.

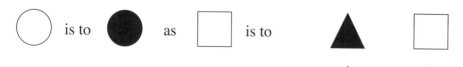

A   **B**   **C**   **D**

The answer is **D** because:-
The second one in each pair is the same shape as the first but with the colour changed to black.

Not A, wrong shape.
Not B, wrong colour.
Not C, wrong shape and colour.

STEP BY STEP

THINGS TO LOOK FOR:-

• CHANGES IN POSITION, COLOUR AND SHAPE

• CHANGES IN THE NUMBER OF SHAPES OR SYMBOLS

• A MIXTURE OF THESE AND OTHER CHANGES

STEP 1:- Find the match between the first pair of shapes.

STEP 2:- Match the second pair in the same way.

STEP 3:- Make sure **all** the necessary changes have been made.

Which shape completes the matching pair? Match the second pair of shapes in the same way as the first. Circle one letter each time. If necessary use the HINTS.

1 [shape] is to [shape] as [circle with N] is to **A** **B** **C** **D**

Find the same shape which is facing the opposite direction.

2 [shape] is to [shape] as [shape] is to **A** **B** **C** **D**

The shape's reflection is joined on.

3 [shape] is to [shape] as [shape] is to **A** **B** **C** **D**

Look at the changes in the position of **all** three shapes.

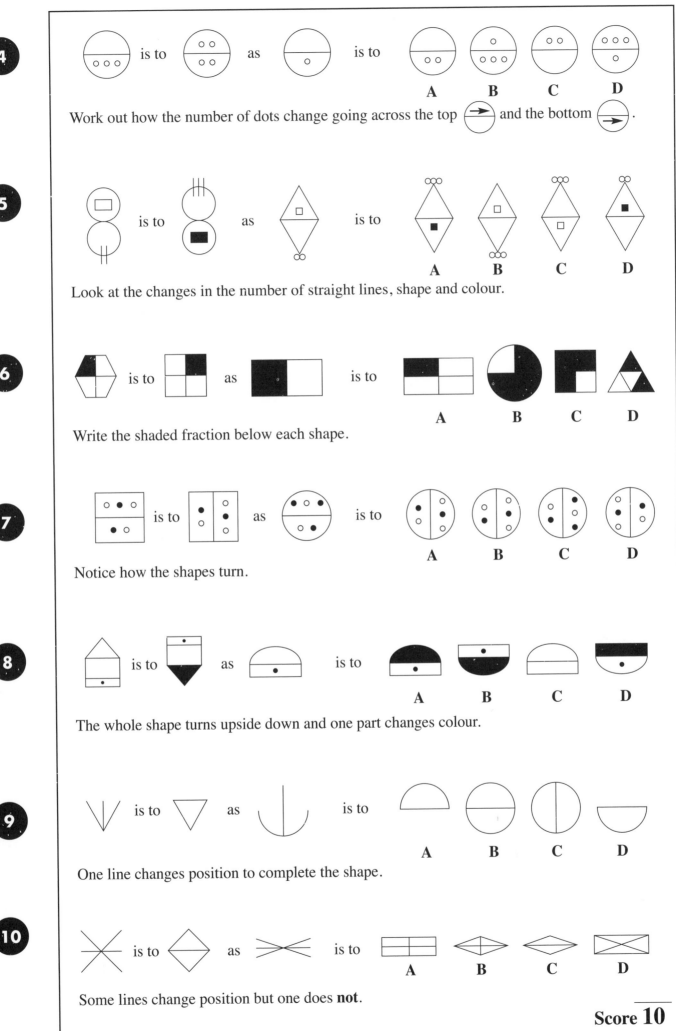

4 Work out how the number of dots change going across the top and the bottom.

5 Look at the changes in the number of straight lines, shape and colour.

6 Write the shaded fraction below each shape.

7 Notice how the shapes turn.

8 The whole shape turns upside down and one part changes colour.

9 One line changes position to complete the shape.

10 Some lines change position but one does **not**.

Score $\overline{10}$

UNIT 17

WHICH TWO SHAPES ARE EXACTLY THE SAME?

Which two shapes are exactly the same? Circle two letters. Look at this example.
(The shapes sometimes turn).

A

Ⓑ

C

D

Ⓔ

The answer is **B** and **E** because:-
When **B** is turned 90° clockwise it is then
seen to be exactly the same as **E.**

Not A, the diagonal lines are different.
Not C or D, the X in both is in a different position.

STEP BY STEP

THINGS TO LOOK FOR:-

• SHAPES CAN BE TURNED EITHER CLOCKWISE ↻ OR ANTI-CLOCKWISE ↺

• often 90° OR 1/4 OF THE WAY ROUND

• and 180° OR 1/2 OF THE WAY ROUND (= UPSIDE DOWN)

• TURNING SHAPES IS DIFFERENT FROM HAVING THE SAME

SHAPE IN THE OPPOSITE DIRECTION, for example:

TURNED   OPPOSITE DIRECTION

STEP 1:- Ignore any diagrams which are obviously different.

STEP 2:- Choose one shape in one of the remaining diagrams to use as a "key".

STEP 3:- Compare this with the position and/or the order of the remaining shapes in each diagram.

STEP 4:- Turn your chosen answers if needed to make sure they are exactly the same.

Which two shapes are exactly the same? The shapes sometimes turn.
Circle two letters each time. If necessary use the HINTS.

❶

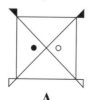
A

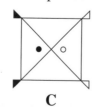
B

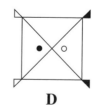
C

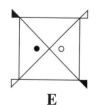
D

E

Look carefully at the 'holes' and 'tips' of each piece.

❷

A

B

C

D

E

Look at the colours of the **small** triangles outside the square.

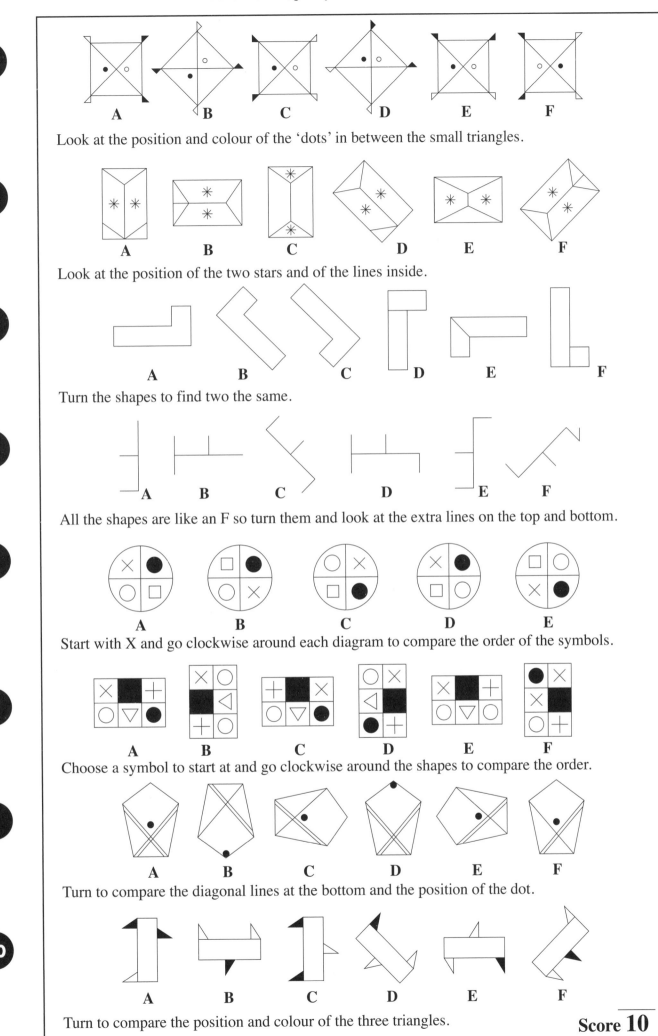

3

Look at the position and colour of the 'dots' in between the small triangles.

4

Look at the position of the two stars and of the lines inside.

5

Turn the shapes to find two the same.

6

All the shapes are like an F so turn them and look at the extra lines on the top and bottom.

7

Start with X and go clockwise around each diagram to compare the order of the symbols.

8

Choose a symbol to start at and go clockwise around the shapes to compare the order.

9

Turn to compare the diagonal lines at the bottom and the position of the dot.

10

Turn to compare the position and colour of the three triangles.

Score 10

UNIT 18

FILL IN THE ADDITION TABLE

Fill in the addition table. Look at this example.

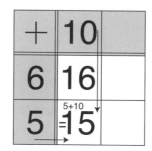

Each table has two sections. The **SUMS SECTION** is coloured **GREY** and gives the numbers to be added. The **ANSWERS SECTION** is **WHITE** and gives the answers to these addition sums.

To fill in the empty WHITE Square, follow the arrows across and down from the **GREY** section and **ADD** these two numbers.

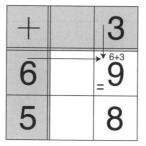

To fill in the empty GREY Square, follow the arrows across and down and work out **what number must be added on**. In the example 6 is added on to 3 to give the answer 9.

STEP BY STEP

STEP 1:- Follow the arrows across and down from the **GREY** section.

STEP 2:- Find the **WHITE** square where the arrows meet.

STEP 3:- Fill in the empty **WHITE** square by adding the two **GREY** numbers from Step 1.

STEP 4:- Fill in the empty **GREY** square, by working out what must be **added on** to the given **GREY** number from Step 1 to get the answer already in the **WHITE** square.

Fill in these addition tables. If necessary use the HINTS.

1

+	4	9
6		15
8	12	

2

+	13	11
5	18	
4		15

Do the addition sums by following the arrows.

3

+		
6	10	15
8	12	17

4

+	13	11
	18	16
	17	15

Work out what must be **added on** to get the number already given in the answers section.

5

+		8
4	9	12
	11	14

6

+	6	
	11	14
3	9	12

Work out what must be **added on** by following the arrows.

7

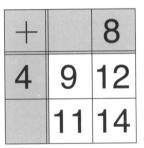

+	9	2
8		10
	20	13

8

+	7	5
	11	9
8	15	

Do **not** mix up the **GREY** sums section with the **WHITE** answers section.

9

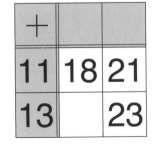

+		
11	18	21
13		23

10

+	4	13
	10	19
	12	

To fill in the **three** empty squares follow the **three** sets of arrows.

Score **10**

HOW WELL DID YOU DO?

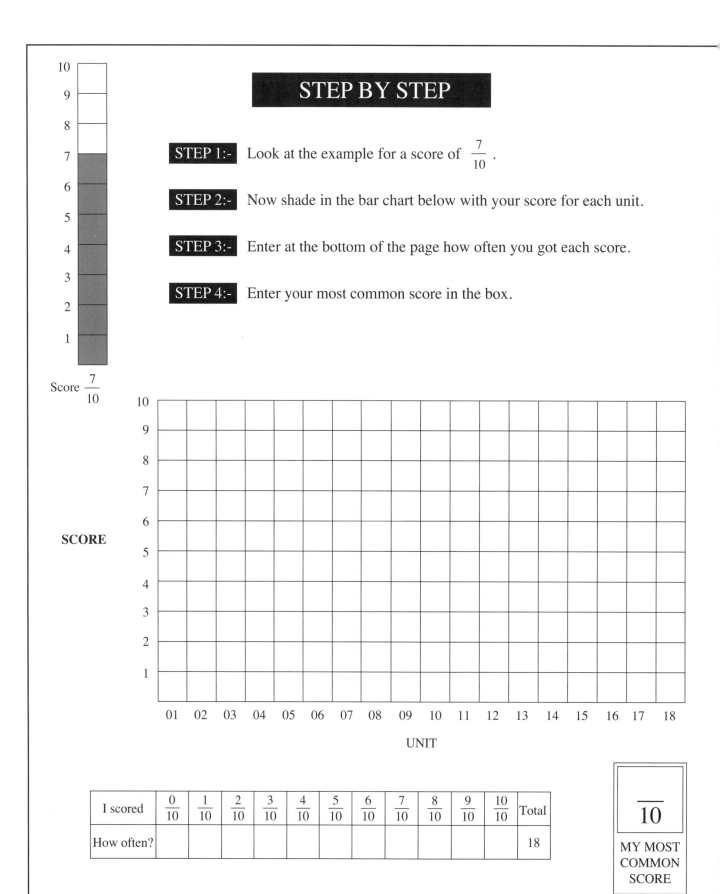

10
9
8
7
6
5
4
3
2
1

Score $\frac{7}{10}$

STEP BY STEP

STEP 1:- Look at the example for a score of $\frac{7}{10}$.

STEP 2:- Now shade in the bar chart below with your score for each unit.

STEP 3:- Enter at the bottom of the page how often you got each score.

STEP 4:- Enter your most common score in the box.

SCORE

10
9
8
7
6
5
4
3
2
1

01 02 03 04 05 06 07 08 09 10 11 12 13 14 15 16 17 18

UNIT

I scored	$\frac{0}{10}$	$\frac{1}{10}$	$\frac{2}{10}$	$\frac{3}{10}$	$\frac{4}{10}$	$\frac{5}{10}$	$\frac{6}{10}$	$\frac{7}{10}$	$\frac{8}{10}$	$\frac{9}{10}$	$\frac{10}{10}$	Total
How often?												18

$\overline{}$
10

MY MOST
COMMON
SCORE

Now you have finished this book, you are ready to start Test 01 in
LEARNING TOGETHER's Practice Tests in Non Verbal Reasoning Book One.

STEP BY STEP NON VERBAL REASONING

ANSWERS

UNIT 1
1. 9
2. 12
3. 13
4. 14
5. 19
6. 18
7. 8
8. 9
9. 7
10. 12

UNIT 2
1. C
2. C
3. D
4. D
5. C
6. D
7. B
8. B
9. B
10. B

UNIT 3
1. $5/6$
2. $3/10$
3. $1/8$
4. $1/8$
5. $1/6$
6. $3/8$
7. $5/11$
8. $4/9$
9. $7/12$
10. $3/16$

UNIT 4
1. C
2. C
3. D
4. D
5. A
6. B
7. E
8. D
9. E
10. A

UNIT 5
1. $3/5$
2. $1/4$
3. $1/2$
4. $1/4$
5. $1/3$
6. $3/4$
7. $2/3$
8. $1/4$
9. $3/4$
10. $2/3$

UNIT 6
1. D
2. B
3. A
4. D
5. C
6. B
7. C
8. D
9. C
10. A

UNIT 7
1. D
2. B
3. A
4. B
5. D
6. C
7. C
8. D
9. B
10. B

UNIT 8
1. 49
2. 20
3. 43
4. 26
5. 17
6. 24
7. 21
8. 30
9. 35
10. 31

UNIT 9
1. C
2. B
3. A
4. B
5. B
6. D
7. B
8. C
9. E
10. E

LEARNING · TOGETHER

STEP BY STEP NON VERBAL REASONING

UNIT 10
1. A
2. D
3. B
4. A
5. D
6. C
7. C
8. A
9. D
10. B

UNIT 11
1. 160
2. 288
3. 243
4. 28
5. 63
6. 3
7. 3
8. 4
9. 8
10. 4

UNIT 12
1. A
2. D
3. C
4. C
5. B
6. C
7. B
8. A
9. D
10. D

UNIT 13
1. B
2. C
3. D
4. D
5. C
6. D
7. A
8. D
9. B
10. A

UNIT 14
1. 3
2. 2
3. 4
4. 8

5.
```
  8 [6]6
  3 1 4
+ 5 1 [1]
1 6 9 1
```

6.
```
  8 [0]9
  5 7 4
+ 2 1 3
1 5 9 6
```

7. 4
8. 7

9.
```
  2 4 8
  [7]6 3
+ 1 4 2
[1]1 5 3
```

10.
```
  4 [2]5
  [6]8 2
+ 1 7 7
[1]2 8 4
```

UNIT 15
1. A
2. B
3. D
4. B
5. B
6. D
7. D
8. B
9. B
10. B

UNIT 16
1. A
2. B
3. C
4. C
5. A
6. D
7. C
8. B
9. D
10. C

UNIT 17
1. A and E
2. B and D
3. A and F
4. B and F
5. B and C
6. C and E
7. A and C
8. A and D
9. C and F
10. D and E

UNIT 18

1. + / 10 / 17
2. + / 16 / 17
3. + / 4 9 / 9
4. + / 5 4 / 9
5. + / 5 / 6
6. + / 5 / 9
7. + / 11 / 17
8. + / 4 / 13
9. + / 7 10 / 20
10. + / 6 / 8 / 21

PUBLISHED BY LEARNING TOGETHER
18 Shandon Park, Belfast BT5 6NW. Phone/fax 028 90402086
www.learningtogether.co.uk email: smcconkey@learningtogether.co.uk
ONLINE PLATFORM: www.onlineelevenplusexams.co.uk

©*Philip Kay BA*